50 Scatter Sheets

About this book

The Scatter Sheets in this book are designed to be used as warm up and theme introduction exercises. They can be used as a quick vocabulary review and fluency exercise or the follow-up questions can be used to underpin a longer and deeper lesson. The core skills practiced are fluency and vocabulary activation therefore they are unsuitable for beginner level classes.

How to use Scatter Sheets

Scatter Sheets are designed to be used as a vocabulary activation exercise. If the vocabulary on the worksheet is totally unfamiliar to the majority of the students then the activity will only cause confusion. If you want to use the Scatter Sheets in this situation, then present the vocabulary items individually to the class before moving on to the describing phase.

Of course there will often be leftover words which are unknown to the whole class and it's the teacher's job to go through these at the end of the exercise.

Give each student a copy of the chosen sheet and give them a few minutes to look at the vocabulary with their neighbour or with a dictionary to see how many words are familiar. Make sure to keep this part short.

Explain that you are going to define a word from the Scatter Sheet and the students must identify it. Describe a word any way you want, for example *it's a type of bird, it hunts at night, there's one in Harry Potter*. If the student's recognise the word *Owl* then they can signal it by shouting out the answer or putting their hand up. If the answer is correct get the students to circle the word *Owl* on their sheets.

Run through the first few examples with stronger students in order to shape some nice example sentences, keep these examples on the board as sentence models.

Students now take it in turns to go through the Scatter Sheet choosing a word which they are comfortable with and describing it to the class. Each word in turn is described and circled until the final words on the sheet are left for the teacher to define.

Extra Questions

Each Scatter Sheet also has an accompanying sheet of extra exercises. The first section is made up of five relatively simple gap fill sentences to further cement the acquisition of some of the lexical items used. The varied grammatical form of these gap-fill sentences could also be used to trigger interesting avenues of grammar or lexical exploration.

This section is followed by three discussion questions which can be done in pairs, groups or together as a class. Listen carefully during this phase, feed in vocabulary where needed and make notes of interesting output that can be expanded on after the discussion phase.

1. The Family

aunt

brother

cousin

daughter

father

grandchildren

grandmother

mother

nephew

niece

sister

son

stepmother

uncle

wife

husband

mother in-law

brother in-law

great grandfather

half sister

1.   The Family

1. Complete the sentences:

a) My brother's daughter is my _ _ _ _ _ _ _ _ _ _ _.

b) My wife's father is my _ _ _ _ _ _ _ _ _ _ _ _ _ _ _ _ _ _ _ _ _.

c) My children's children are my _.

d) My father's sister is my _ _ _ _ _ _ _ _ _ _.

e) My uncle's children are my _ _ _ _ _ _ _ _ _ _.

2. Discussion questions

a) Who are the youngest and oldest people in your family?

b) Does your family get together often? Do you get on well together?

c) Is family important?

2.   On the Internet

browser

scrollbar

window

search engine

checkbox

form

field

tab

bookmark

the cloud

blog

mobile site

stream

e-mail

podcast

social network

URL

homepage

comment

link

2.   On the Internet

1. Complete the sentences:

a) Facebook, Twitter and Google Plus are all _ _ _ _ _ _ _ _ _ _ _ _ _ _ _ _ _ _ _.

b) A _ _ _ _ _ _ _ _ _ _ _ is like a radio show on the internet.

c) *What's the* _ _ _ _ _ _ _ ? is another way of asking *what's the web address?*

d) If you want to save a webpage to read later you can _ _ _ _ _ _ _ _ _ _ it.

e) One way to backup your files is to save them in _ _ _ _ _ _ _ _ _ _ _ _ _ _ _.

2. Discussion questions

a) Are you happy to store important information in the cloud?

b) Do you listen to any podcasts?

c) Are you a member of any social networks?

3. Websites

YouTube

Twitter

Yahoo

Facebook

Google

Flickr

Amazon

eBay

PayPal

Wikipedia

Bing

Tumblr

Pinterest

Reddit

Blogger

Baidu

Instagram

Wordpress

Netflix

Craigslist

3.   Websites

1. Complete the sentences:

a) _ _ _ _ _ _ _ _ is an online auction site.

b) _ _ _ _ _ _ _ _ is a good source of information on almost anything.

c) _ _._ _ _ _ _ _ _ _ _ is the most popular social network in the world.

d) _ _ _ _ _ _ _ is a rival to Google's search engine.

e) _ _ _ _ _ _ _ _ _ _ _ is a popular online payment system.

2. Discussion questions

a) Which websites do you spend the most time on?

b) Do you buy much online? Which sites do you use?

c) Have you ever had a blog? Which blogs do you follow?

4.   Information Technology

application

browser

bug

cookie

crash

cursor

driver

FAQ

firewall

font

hardware

click

homepage

cable

software

scanner

spam

virus

delete

password

4.   Information Technology

1. Complete the sentences:

a) To physically connect one piece of hardware with another, you will need the right

_ _ _ _ _ _ _ _ _ _.

b) *Arial*, *Georgia* and *Verdana* are all types of _ _ _ _ _ _ _ _ _ _.

c) To connect a new piece of hardware to your computer, you often need to install the right

_ _ _ _ _ _ _ _ _ _ _ .

d) Unwanted, unimportant e-mail is often called _ _ _ _ _ _ _ _ _.

e) If you have too many programs running, your computer might _ _ _ _ _ _ _ _ _.

2. Discussion questions

a) What's your homepage?

b) Can you remember the first computer you owned or used?

c) What do you find frustrating about using computers?

5.   Jobs

Lawyer

Software Developer

Politician

Estate Agent

Travel Agent

Scientist

Vet

Nurse

Doctor

Accountant

Lecturer

Actor

Entrepreneur

Graphic Designer

Social Worker

Receptionist

Journalist

Illustrator

Plumber

Decorator

5.   Jobs

1. Complete the sentences:

a) A _ _ _ _ _ _ _ _ _ _ _ _ _ _ _ _ _ _ is someone who paints your house.

b) A person who starts new businesses is called an _ _ _ _ _ _ _ _ _ _ _ _ _ _ _ _ _ _.

c) An _ _ _ _ _ _ _ _ _ _ _ _ _ _ _ _ 's drawings are often used in books and magazines .

d) You could go to a _ _ _ _ _ _ _ _ _ _ _ _ _ _ _ _ _ if you want to book a holiday.

e) A _ _ _ _ _ looks after sick animals.

2. Discussion questions

a) What was your first job?

b) What do you like/dislike about your job?

c) What job would you really like to have?

6. In the Office

clock

monitor

laptop

printer

whiteboard

meeting

presentation

canteen

coffee break

lift

reception

calendar

photocopier

filing cabinet

office draw

fax machine

wastepaper basket

shredder

open-plan

boss

6.   In the Office

1. Complete the sentences:

a) Confidential documents should be disposed of with a _ _ _ _ _ _ _ _ _ _ _ _ _ .

b) Hard copies of customer records are often kept in a _ _ _ _ _ _ _ _ _ _ _ _ _ _ _ _ _ .

c) If you don't want to take the stairs, you can use the _ _ _ _ _ _ _ _ _ _ _ _ _ _ .

d) Some companies *still* use a _ _ _ _ _ _ _ _ _ _ _ _ _ _ _ _ to send documents.

e) Office workers often keep their belongings in their _ _ _ _ _ _ _ _ _ _ _ _ _ _ _ _ _ .

2. Discussion questions

a) Would you rather work in an open plan office or have your own office?

b) Have you ever worked in an office? Did you like it?

c) Is there a lot of paperwork in your current or last job?

7.   Stationery

stapler

envelope

diary

calendar

folder

hole punch

pencil

paperclip

shredder

stamp

scissors

glue

drawing pin

sticky tape

rubber band

post-it note

notebook

ruler

clipboard

eraser

7. Stationery

1. Complete the sentences:

a) Use a pair of _ _ _ _ _ _ _ _ _ _ _ _ if you want to cut something out.

b) If you're going to send a letter, you'll need to put a _ _ _ _ _ _ _ _ _ on the envelope.

c) You can use a _ _ _ _ _ _ _ _ _ _ _ _ _ to attach one document to another.

d) If you want to draw a straight line, use a _ _ _ _ _ _ _ _ .

e) People often use a _ _ _ _ _ _ _ _ _ _ _ _ _ _ to remind themselves to do

something.

2. Discussion questions

a) Do you carry a notebook? What do you write in it?

b) What do you use to keep track of your appointments?

c) Would you describe yourself or your workplace as well organised?

8.   In the Lab

test tube

scientist

experiment

result

invention

calculation

physicist

biologist

chemistry

acid

equipment

gravity

equation

cell

microscope

clone

specimen

goggles

ventilator

fire extinguisher

8. In the Lab

1. Complete the sentences:

a) _ _ _ _ _ _ _ _ _ _ _ is a force that attracts objects to each other.

b) If you are working with dangerous substances, you should wear _ _ _ _ _ _ _ _ _ _ _ _.

c) $E = mc^2$ is Einstein's most famous _ _ _ _ _ _ _ _ _ _ _ _ _ _ _ _ _ _.

d) _ _ _ _ _ _ _ _ is the opposite of alkaline.

e) A _ _ _ _ _ _ _ _ _ _ _ _ _ _ _ _ _ _ is a device that freshens the air in a room.

2. Discussion questions

a) What do you think are the most important inventions of the last ten years?

b) What life-changing inventions or discoveries might be made in the next ten?

c) What scientists or scientific discoveries come from your country?

9.   Brands

Google

BMW

Ferrari

Coca Cola

Apple

Samsung

Pepsi

McDonalds

Disney

Sony

Toyota

Mercedes

Gillette

Yves Saint Laurent

Nescafe

Budweiser

L'Oreal

Ikea

Nike

Levis

9.   Brands

1. Complete the sentences:

a) _ _ _ _ _ _ _ _ _ _ _ _ is famous for its shaving products.

b) _ _ _ _ _ _ _ _ _ _ _ is well known for its flat-pack furniture.

c) _ _ _ _ _ _ _ _ _ _ _ has several large amusement parks around the world.

d) _ _ _ _ _ _ _ _ _ and _ _ _ _ _ _ _ _ _ are great rivals in the soft drinks market.

e) _ _ _ _ _ _ _ _ _ is famous for its denim clothing.

2. Discussion questions

a) Which brands do you use the most?

b) Do you prefer branded food products to supermarkets' own label products?

c) What do you think are high-status brands?

10. Meetings and Presentations

slide

presenter

attendees

agenda

the minutes

chairperson

demonstration

report

chart

projector

powerpoint

discussion

argument

negotiation

deal

speech

prototype

flipchart

vote

confidential

10.   Meetings and Presentations

1. Complete the sentences:

a) _ _ _ _ _ _ _ _ _ _ _ _ _ _ _ _ _ is another word for secret.

b) If all sides agree they may shake hands and make a _ _ _ _ _ _ _ _ _.

c) The people who are present at a meeting are the _ _ _ _ _ _ _ _ _ _ _ _ _ _.

d) Keeping a record of what is said in a meeting is called *taking* _ _ _ _ _ _ _ _ _ _ _ _ .

e) A _ _ _ _ _ _ _ _ _ is a diagram which shows information.

2. Discussion questions

a) How often do you attend meetings? What percentage are a waste of time?

b) What do you do if you get bored in a long meeting?

c) Public speaking is one of people's greatest fears. Is it one of yours?

11.   Law and Order

police

court

judge

case

lawyer

defendant

prison

sentence

guilty

innocent

jury

under arrest

witness

trial

bail

suspect

alibi

crime

charge

evidence

11.   Law and Order

1. Complete the sentences:

a) The place where cases are heard is called a _ _ _ _ _ _ _ _ _ _ _ .

b) The person in charge of the court is the _ _ _ _ _ _ _ _ _ _ _.

c) A _ _ _ _ _ _ _ _ _ _ _ _ is a person who saw a crime take place.

d) _ _ _ _ _ _ _ _ _ _ _ _ _ is produced in court to prove whether the defendant is

guilty or innocent.

e) If the defendant is found guilty, they may get a long _ _ _ _ _ _ _ _ _ _ _ sentence.

2. Discussion questions

a) Have you ever been to court?

b) If you had the power to make something illegal, what would it be?

c) Is it sometimes okay to break a law?

Crime and Punishment

murder

assault

mugger

robbery

death penalty

life sentence

a fine

shoplifter

thief

pickpocket

arson

blackmail

fraud

vandalism

burglar

drug dealer

victim

kidnapping

counterfeiter

identity theft

12.   Crime and Punishment

1. Complete the sentences:

a) If you are caught speeding, you may have to pay _ _   _ _ _ _ _ _ _.

b) Somebody who makes copies of products or money is a _ _ _ _ _ _ _ _ _ _ _ _ _ _ _ _ _.

c) A person who breaks into a house to steal things is called a _ _ _ _ _ _ _ _ _ _ _ _ _ _.

d) In some states of the USA the _ _ _ _ _ _ _ _   _ _ _ _ _ _ _ _ _ _ is carried out by

electric chair or lethal injection .

e) _ _ _ _ _ _ _ _ _ _ _ _   _ _ _ _ _ _ _ is when someone pretends to be another person.

2. Discussion questions

a) Have you ever had anything stolen?

b) Do you think graffiti is vandalism or art?

c) What would you do if you saw someone being mugged?

13.   Money

wallet

purse

banknote

coin

credit card

gift voucher

change

bills

receipt

currency

bank account

cash machine / ATM

debt

interest

loan

mortgage

wages

profit

deposit

poor

valuable

13.   Money

1. Complete the sentences:

a) _ _ _ _ _ _ _ _ are paid by your employer in exchange for your work.

b) The dollar is the _ _ _ _ _ _ _ _ _ _ _ _ _ _ of the USA

c) If you keep your money in a savings account you will receive _ _ _ _ _ _ _ _ _ _ _ _ _ _.

d) Instead of money, you might get a _ _ _ _ _ _ _ _ _ _ _ _ _ _ _ _ _ for your birthday.

e) If you want to rent an apartment you have to put down a _ _ _ _ _ _ _ _ _ _ _ _ first.

2. Discussion questions

a) How much money are you carrying at the moment?

b) If you had $100,000 would you put it in a savings account or invest it somewhere else?

c) Do you think people will still use coins and banknotes in 20 years?

14.   At the Zoo

giraffe

monkey

crocodile

snake

tortoise

lion

tiger

lizard

rhinoceros

elephant

hippopotamus

wolf

eagle

owl

seal

cheetah

penguin

flamingo

bear

zebra

14.   At the Zoo

1. Complete the sentences:

a A _ _ _ _ _ _ _ _ _ _ _ has a very long neck.

b) A _ _ _ _ _ _ _ _ _ _ _ _ is a flightless bird which lives in Antarctica

c) An _ _ _ _ _ _ _ is a bird which hunts at night.

d) A _ _ _ _ _ _ _ _ _ _ _ is the fastest animal on land.

e) A _ _ _ _ _ _ _ _ _ has black and white stripes.

2. Discussion questions

a) Does your country have an animal as a national symbol?

b) Do you think animals should be kept in zoos?

c) What's your favourite animal?

15. The Countryside

river

autumn

clouds

landscape

view

hills

stream

bush

reflection

forest

field

lake

path

wildlife

birdsong

sunset

dawn

mist

rainbow

sheep

15. The Countryside

1. Complete the sentences:

a) _ _ _ _ _ _ _ _ _ and _ _ _ _ _ _ _ _ _ _ could both be described as white and fluffy.

b) You might see a _ _ _ _ _ _ _ _ _ _ _ _ _ when it stops raining and the sun comes out.

c) At the end of the day you might see a beautiful _ _ _ _ _ _ _ _ _ _ _ _.

d) You can have a great _ _ _ _ _ _ _ _ from the top of a hill or mountain.

e) Animals, birds, plants and flowers are all examples of an area's _ _ _ _ _ _ _ _ _ _ _ _.

2. Discussion questions

a) Can you remember an amazing view you have seen.

b) Do you have a favourite plant or flower?

c) Do you prefer to go for walks in the town or the country?

16.　Sea Life

submarine

whale

octopus

cruise ship

shark

harbour

yacht

lighthouse

lobster

seagull

tanker

jellyfish

coral

shells

turtle

oyster

pelican

aquarium

shipwreck

diver

16.   Sea Life

1. Complete the sentences:

a) A _ _ _ _ _ _ _ _ _ _ _ _ _ _ is a type of ship that can travel underwater.

b) A _ _ _ _ _ _ _ _ _ _ _ _ _ is a tall building with a bright lamp at the top.

c) A _ _ _ _ _ _ _ _ _ _ _ _ _ is a big ship which carries liquid, usually oil.

d) A _ _ _ _ _ _ _ _ _ is a big fish which sometimes eats people.

e) A _ _ _ _ _ _ _ _ _ _ is like a car park for ships.

2. Discussion questions

a) Have you ever been on a cruise?

b) What's the tastiest thing that lives in the sea?

c) Would you like to go to the bottom of the ocean in a submarine?

17.   Up in the Sky

Jumbo Jet

helicopter

eagle

rocket

kite

air balloon

planet

a fly

star

the sun

rainbow

butterfly

UFO

frisbee

parachute

cloud

airship

missile

satellite

meteorite

17.   Up in the Sky

1. Complete the sentences:

a) If you jump out of an aeroplane, you will need a _ _ _ _ _ _ _ _ _ _ _ _ _ _ _.

b) A _ _ _ _ _ _ _ _ _ _ _ is a weapon which can travel a great distance.

c) Some people like to play with a _ _ _ _ _ _ _ _ _ _ _ at the park or on the beach.

d) The Earth, Mars and Jupiter are all _ _ _ _ _ _ _ _ _ _.

e) A _ _ _ _ _ _ _ _ _ _ _ _ _ _ _ _ _ _ has a rotor and can take off and land vertically.

2. Discussion questions

a) Do you like flying? What's the longest flight you've been on?

b) Would you like to fly in an air balloon?

c) If you had a spaceship, where would you travel to first?

18.   Transport

lorry

train

hitchhiker

underground

helicopter

tram

ship

hot air balloon

ferry

jet ski

motorbike

submarine

spaceship

tank

sledge

camel

horse

bus

bicycle

skateboard

18. Transport

1. Complete the sentences:

a) A _ _ _ _ _ _ _ _ _ _ _ _ _ _ _ is like a bicycle with an engine.

b) A _ _ _ _ _ _ _ _ is like a motorbike that goes on water.

c) A _ _ _ _ _ _ _ _ is like a bus that travels on water.

d) A _ _ _ _ _ _ _ is an armoured military vehicle with a large gun mounted to it.

e) When it snows you can take your _ _ _ _ _ _ _ _ _ to the top of a hill to have some fun.

2. Discussion questions

a) Have you ever ridden on an animal?

b) Have you ever owned a motorbike?

c) What's your favourite form of transport?

19.   The Car

pedal

steering wheel

wing mirror

clutch

brake

accelerator

boot

bonnet

gear stick

reverse

indicator

headlights

bumper

speedometer

rear view mirror

engine

petrol tank

spare wheel

handbrake

windscreen

19.   The Car

1. Complete the sentences:

a) If you want to see who's behind you, check your _ _ _ _ _ _ _ _ _ _ _ _ _ _ _ _ _ _ .

b) _ _ _ _ _ _ _ _ _ _ _ means to go backwards.

c) If you want to go faster, put your foot on the _ _ _ _ _ _ _ _ _ _ _ _ _ _ _ _ _ _ _.

d) The _ tells you how fast you are going.

e) Don't forget to use your _ _ _ _ _ _ _ _ _ _ _ _ _ before turning left or right.

2. Discussion questions

a) If you could have any car, what would you like to drive?

b) How do you think cars might change in the next ten to twenty years?

c) What annoying things do car drivers do?

20. Travel

passport

suitcase

ticket

airport

luggage

hotel

hostel

journey

daytrip

flight

hike

departures

arrivals

accommodation

guidebook

sightseeing

reservation

adventure

package holiday

customs

20. Travel

1. Complete the sentences:

a) Hotels, hostels and apartments are all forms of _.

b) You usually need to show your _ _ _ _ _ _ _ _ _ _ _ _ _ _ when travelling to other countries.

c) When you return from a trip abroad, you have to go through _ _ _ _ _ _ _ _ _ _ _ _ _.

d) If you want to stay at a hotel, you will usually need a _ _ _ _ _ _ _ _ _ _ _ _ _ _ _ _ _ _.

e) A _ _ _ _ _ _ _ _ _ is a long walk in the countryside.

2. Discussion questions

a) If you could visit any city / country in the world, where would you go?

b) Have you had any travel nightmares?

c) What's the most memorable journey you've been on?

21. Countries

England

Germany

China

USA

North Korea

Spain

Brazil

Sweden

Turkey

Australia

Canada

France

Japan

Russia

Scotland

India

Zimbabwe

Mexico

Pakistan

South Africa

21.   Countries

1. Complete the sentences:

a) _ _ _ _ _ _ _ _ _ _ _ is famous for its spicy curries.

b) _ _ _ _ _ _ _ _ _ _ _ _ _ _ is the home of kilts, whisky, golf and the Loch Ness Monster.

c) _ _ _ _ _ _ _ _ _ _ _ _ is in North America and is the second biggest country in the world.

d) _ _ _ _ _ _ _ _ _ _ _ _ _ is well known for producing good quality cars, for example

BMW and Mercedes are from this country.

e) _ _ _ _ _ _ _ _ _ is famous for its carnival, great beaches and a magnificent football team.

2. Discussion questions

a) If you had to live in another country for a few years, where would you choose?

b) What's the most expensive country you have visited?

c) What is your country well known for?

22.   In the Bathroom

tap

plug

sink

toothbrush

toothpaste

soap

bathroom cabinet

bath mat

shampoo

razor

shaving foam

moisturiser

nail clippers

electric shaver

conditioner

cotton wool

deodorant

towel

shower gel

bathrobe

22.   In the Bathroom

1. Complete the sentences:

a) You put _ _ _ _ _ _ _ _ _ _ _ _ _ on your hair after you have washed it with shampoo.

b) A _ _ _ _ _ _ _ _ _ _ is sharp and used for getting rid of unwanted hair.

c) _ _ _ _ _ _ _ _ _ _ _ _ _ _ _ _ keeps you smelling good all day.

d) If you are wet you need a _ _ _ _ _ _ _ _ _ _ to make you dry.

e) You put a _ _ _ _ _ _ _ _ in the sink to stop the water draining away.

2. Discussion questions

a) Do you prefer baths or showers?

b) Do you try to save water?

c) Have you ever had a cold bath or shower?

23.

In the Kitchen

saucepan

wooden spoon

frying pan

sieve

scales

tin opener

jar

oven glove

chopping board

microwave

apron

tea towel

blender

ladle

teaspoon

herbs

baking tray

kettle

jug

rolling pin

23. In the Kitchen

1. Complete the sentences:

a) A _ _ _ _ _ _ _ _ _ _ _ _ _ _ _ _ _ _ cooks food much faster than a normal oven.

b) Use a _ _ _ _ _ _ _ _ _ _ _ _ _ _ to stir your tea or coffee.

c) You can boil water quickly and easily with a _ _ _ _ _ _ _ _ _ _ _.

d) A _ _ _ _ _ _ _ _ _ _ _ is a kitchen gadget which cuts food into very small pieces.

e) If you are taking hot things out of the oven you will need an _ _ _ _ _ _ _ _ _ _ _ _ _ .

2. Discussion questions

a) Do you like cooking? What's your signature dish?

b) Who's the best cook you know?

c) What's the last thing you cooked?

24.   In the Bedroom

sheets

blanket

bedside lamp

pillow

chest of drawers

wardrobe

coat hanger

mattress

duvet

alarm clock

mirror

curtains

rug

dressing table

hair brush

make-up

clothes

hair dryer

slippers

dressing gown

24.   In the Bedroom

1. Complete the sentences:

a) *Get dressed* is another way of saying *put your* _ _ _ _ _ _ _ _ _ _ _ _ _ _ *on*.

b) Lipstick, mascara and eyeliner are all types of _ _ _ _ _ _ _ _ _ _ _ _ _ _.

c) _ _ _ _ _ _ _ _ _ _ _ _ _ _ are shoes that you wear in the house.

d) *Draw the* _ _ _ _ _ _ _ _ _ _ in the evening to stop people looking in your windows.

e) You put your head on a _ _ _ _ _ _ _ _ _ _ _ _ when you go to sleep.

2. Discussion questions

a) How long does it take you to fall asleep in the evening?

b) How much sleep do you need? How do you feel if you don't get it?

c) What's your favourite room in your home?

25.   In the Garage

lawnmower

rake

spade

sledge

paint

tools

bicycle

broken TV

old magazines

surfboard

rubber boots

kite

model boat

freezer

wheelbarrow

ladder

workbench

dart board

chainsaw

axe

25.   In the Garage

1. Complete the sentences:

a) On a windy day you can go to the park and fly a _ _ _ _ _ _ _ _.

b) Use an _ _ _ _ _ _ _ if you need to chop down a tree.

c) A _ _ _ _ _ _ _ _ _ _ _ _ _ _ _ _ _ _ _ has one wheel and is used for transporting things

in the garden.

d) A _ _ _ _ _ _ _ _ _ _ _ _ _ _ _ _ keeps food very cold.

e) With a _ _ _ _ _ _ _ _ _ _ _ _ _ _ _ you can reach high places.

2. Discussion questions

a) Do you have a garage or a cellar? What do you keep in it?

b) Do you like to hang on to old things or throw them away?

c) What's the oldest thing you own?

26.   In the Garden

hosepipe

sprinkler

birdhouse

squirrel

barbecue

vegetable patch

shed

greenhouse

butterfly

wasps

fishpond

compost heap

path

patio

flower pot

garden furniture

fox

nest

spade

weeds

26.   In the Garden

1. Complete the sentences:

a) A _ is a little house made of glass.

b) You need a _ _ _ _ _ _ _ _ _ if you want to dig a hole.

c) _ _ _ _ _ _ _ _ _ _ are unwanted plants.

d) Follow the _ _ _ _ _ _ _ _ _ _ to get across the garden without treading on the grass.

e) _ _ _ _ _ _ _ _ _ _ _ _s live in trees, eat nuts and go to sleep in the winter.

2. Discussion questions

a) Describe your dream garden.

b) Do you have a favourite plant, tree or flower?

c) Do you think there are enough green areas where you live?

27.   Sports and Games

football / soccer

volleyball

chess

poker

rugby

baseball

Monopoly

polo

the Olympics

sprint

pool

Tetris

Super Mario

basketball

hockey

boxing

tennis

long jump

bowling

golf

27.   Sports and Games

1. Complete the sentences:

a) A _ _ _ _ _ _ _ _ _ is a short distance running race.

b) _ _ _ _ _ _ _ _ _ _ is a sport played with a ball, two or four rackets and a net.

c) The person with all the money is the winner of the board game _ _ _ _ _ _ _ _ _ _ _ .

d) _ _ _ _ _ _ _ is played on a table with pockets, with a cue and different coloured balls.

e) _ _ _ _ _ _ _ _ _ is a game of strategy, pawns, kings and queens are part of the game.

2. Discussion questions

a) Do you play or watch any sports?

b) Do you play video games?

c) What games did you like to play when you were a child?

28. Exercise

jogging

hiking

walking

swimming

gym

weight lifting

aerobics

yoga

karate

press ups

cycling

treadmill

climbing

boxing

inline skating

shopping

mountain biking

trampolining

skipping

marathon

28. Exercise

1. Complete the sentences:

a) A _ _ _ _ _ _ _ _ _ _ _ _ _ is a machine that lets you run without going anywhere.

b) Jumping up and down on a stretched rubber sheet is called _ _ _ _ _ _ _ _ _ _ _ _ _ _ _.

c) _ _ _ _ _ _ _ _ _ _ _ _ _ _ _ _ _ _ _ _ _ _ _ _ _ is the best way to build up muscle.

d) A _ _ _ _ _ is a special room where you can use machines to help you get fit.

e) _ _ _ _ _ _ _ _ _ _ is a martial art that you wear padded gloves to do.

2. Discussion questions

a) Do you get enough exercise? What types of exercise do you like to do?

b) Would you rather exercise in a gym or outside?

c) What advice would you give someone who doesn't do any exercise?

29. Hobbies

calligraphy

skiing

embroidery

skydiving

skateboarding

collecting

painting

drawing

reading

cinema

gardening

travelling

photography

cooking

knitting

shopping

DIY

pottery

learning languages

going to the gym

29.   Hobbies

1. Complete the sentences:

a) _ _ _ _ _ is improving the place where you live.

b) Creating pictures with a pencil is known as _ _ _ _ _ _ _ _ _ _ _ _ _ _ _ _ _ _ _.

c) _ _ _ _ _ _ _ _ _ _ _ _ _ _ _ is the art of making pots, bowls, vases, etc.

d) _ _ _ _ _ _ _ _ _ _ _ _ _ _ _ is the art of writing beautifully.

e) Planting, pruning, trimming and mowing are all parts of _ _ _ _ _ _ _ _ _ _ _ _ _ _ _ _.

2. Discussion questions

a) Do you have any hobbies?

b) Have you ever collected anything?

c) If you didn't have to work, how would you fill your free-time?

30. Going out

dancing

bowling

cinema

theatre

concert

casino

musical

pub / bar

dinner party

comedy show

book club

poker night

art gallery

museum

opera

pool hall

ping pong

language class

cocktail bar

karaoke

30.   Going out

1. Complete the sentences:

a) Margarita, Manhattan, Mojito and Cosmopolitan are all types of _ _ _ _ _ _ _ _ _ _ _ _ .

b) At an _ _ _ _ _ _   _ _ _ _ _ _ _ _ _ _ _ _ _ _ you might see paintings or sculptures.

c) At a _ _ _ _ _ _ _ _ _ _ you might play poker, blackjack or roulette.

d) In _ _ _ _ _ _ _ _ _ _ you have to knock down ten pins to get the highest score.

e) If you like singing you could go to a _ _ _ _ _ _ _ _ _ _ _ _ _ _ bar.

2. Discussion questions

a) What's your idea of a good night out?

b) If you could go to any concert, museum, gallery, sporting event etc. what would you see?

c) Do you have any recommendations for a nice day out in your town or city?

31. In the Supermarket

trolley

shelves

freezer

aisle

checkout

the till

carrier bag

shop assistant

store detective

basket

dairy products

confectionary

coupon

special offer

out of stock

manager

opening hours

queue

receipt

change

31.   In the Supermarket

1. Complete the sentences:

a) If the supermarket is busy, there might be a _ _ _ _ _ _ _ _ _ _ _ at the checkout.

b) After you pay, the cashier will give you your change and a _ _ _ _ _ _ _ _ _ _ _.

c) Milk, cheese, butter and yoghurt are all types of _ .

d) If there's a _ _ _ _ _ _ _ _ _ _ _ _ _ _ _ you might get some items cheaper than usual.

e) If a product is _ _ _ _ _ _ _ _ _ _ _ _ _, there are none left to buy.

2. Discussion questions

a) Where do you do your grocery shopping?

b) Do you try to buy organic or local products?

c) How would you improve your local supermarket?

The High Street

post office

bakery

supermarket

optician

butcher

stationer

chemist

florist

barber shop

DIY store

tailor

cafe

restaurant

bar / pub

library

museum

gallery

department store

jeweler

newsagent

32.   The High Street

1. Complete the sentences:

a) If you're looking for a wedding ring, you need to visit a _ _ _ _ _ _ _ _ _ _ _ _ _ _ _.

b) You can find tools, screws, wood and paint at a _ _ _ _ _ _ _ _ _ _ _ _ _ _ _ _ _.

c) Buy some flowers for a loved one at the _ _ _ _ _ _ _ _ _ _ _ _ _.

d) Men can have a suit made at a _ _ _ _ _ _ _ _ _ _ _.

e) If you want to buy some meat, visit a _ _ _ _ _ _ _ _ _ _ _ _ _.

2. Discussion questions

a) What do you enjoy shopping for?

b) Do you do a lot of shopping online?

c) Do you like to go shopping on holiday?

33.   In the Street

truck

lamp post

post box

pavement

van

zebra crossing

traffic lights

road sign

billboard

car park

roadworks

bridge

school

pedestrians

wall

junction

demonstration

traffic warden

speed bumps

shops

33.   In the Street

1. Complete the sentences:

a) If you want to send a letter, put it in a _ _ _ _ _ _ _   _ _ _ _ _.

b) If you want to cross a river, you'll need to find a _ _ _ _ _ _ _ _ _ _ _.

c) People who are walking in the street are called _ _ _ _ _ _ _ _ _ _ _ _ _ _ _ _ _ _ _.

d) A _ _ _ _ _ _ _ _ _ _ _   _ _ _ _ _ _ _ _ _ _ _ _ gives tickets to people who park in

the wrong place

e) A _ _ _ _ _ _ _ _ _   _ _ _ _ _ _ _ _ _ _ tells you where to go or what to do.

2. Discussion questions

a) Describe the street where you live. Is it quiet or noisy?

b) What one thing would most improve your street?

c) How could your town be improved for drivers and pedestrians?

34.   Christmas

angel

stocking

elves

reindeer

presents

nativity scene

Father Christmas

chimney

Christmas card

candle

mistletoe

cracker

sleigh

snow

star

Christmas Eve

tinsel

snowman

carol

Boxing Day

34.　Christmas

1. Complete the sentences:

a) Hang up a _ _ _ _ _ _ _ _on Xmas Eve and Father Christmas might fill it with presents.

b) A Christmas _ _ _ _ _ _ _ _ _ is a song with a Christmas theme.

c) The day after Christmas day is called _ _ _ _ _ _ _ _ _ _ _ _ _ _ _ _.

d) A _ _ _ _ _ _ _ _ _ _ _ is made of wax and you light one end of it.

e) Father Christmas rides a _ _ _ _ _ _ _ _ _ _ towed by reindeers.

2. Discussion questions

a) Do you celebrate Christmas? What do you enjoy about this time?

b) What is the best present you have ever been given?

c) What other festivals are celebrated in your country?

35.   Famous People

Neil Armstrong

Yuri Gagarin

Albert Einstein

Muhammad Ali

Bruce Lee

Bob Marley

Queen Elizabeth II

Cleopatra

Hillary Clinton

Paul McCartney

Marilyn Monroe

Christopher Columbus

Madonna

Shakespeare

JK Rowling

Leonardo da Vinci

Julius Caesar

Mahatma Gandhi

Pele

Nelson Mandela

35.   Famous People

1. Complete the sentences:

a) _ _ _ _ _ _ _ _ _ _ _ _ _ _ _ _ _ _ _ was the first person to travel into space.

b) _ _ _ _ _ _ is sometimes described as the greatest footballer who ever lived.

c) _ _ _ _ _ _ _ _ _ _ _ _ _ _ _ _ _ _ is famous for being a Beatle.

d) _ _ _ _ _ _ _ _ _ _ _ _ _ _ _ _ was one of the pioneers of reggae music.

e) _ _ _ _ _ _ _ _ _ _ _ _ _ _ _ _ _ _ _ was a famous actress from the 1950s

2. Discussion questions

a) Which people, living or dead, do you most admire?

b) Do you have a favourite actor or actress?

c) Who are the most famous people from your town / city or country?

Special Occasions

Christmas

Easter

Ramadan

New Years Day

birthday

wedding

anniversary

baptism / christening

graduation

retirement

funeral

engagement

Halloween

carnival

party

housewarming

baby shower

reunion

stag night

festival

36. Special Occasions

1. Complete the sentences:

a) Someone with a new home might invite you to a _ _ _ _ _ _ _ _ _ _ _ _ _ _ _ party.

b) Sometimes a man will have a _ _ _ _ _ _   _ _ _ _ _ _ _ _ before he gets married.

c) Couples celebrate their _ _ _ _ _ _ _ _ _ _ _ _ _ _ when they decide to get married.

d) _ _ _ _ _ _ _ _ _ _ _ _ is a month of fasting celebrated by Muslims.

e) As people come towards the end of their working lives they begin to look forward to their

_ _ _ _ _ _ _ _ _ _ _ _ _ _ _ _.

2. Discussion questions

a) Have you ever thrown a party, on what occasion?

b) Do men or women in your culture have something similar to a stag night?

c) How do you think you'll spend your retirement?

37. In a Toolbox

screwdriver

hammer

drill

spanner / wrench

screws

nails

nuts and bolts

wire

saw

spirit level

tape measure

string

glue

fuse

sandpaper

raw plug

pencil

soldering iron

safety goggles

knife

37.   In a Toolbox

1. Complete the sentences:

a) You should wear _ _ _ _ _ _ _ _ _ _   _ _ _ _ _ _ _ _ _ _ _ _ to protect your eyes.

b) You can use _ _ _ _ _ _ _ _ _ _ _ _ _ to make something smooth.

c) _ _ _ _ _ _ is used to stick things together.

d) If you want to make a hole in a wall, you'll probably need a _ _ _ _ _ _ _.

e) Try not to hit your thumb when you're using a _ _ _ _ _ _ _ _ _ _ _.

2. Discussion questions

a) Do you try to fix things yourself when they break?

b) Do you have a lot of tools? Which is the most useful?

c) What do people say when they hit their thumb with a hammer in your native language?

Toys and Games

doll

action figure

costume

ball

crayons

plasticine

yo-yo

walkie talkies

rubber duck

teddy bear

rattle

dinosaur

robot

lego

balloon

drum

bicycle

scooter

toy farm

magic wand

38.   Toys and Games

1. Complete the sentences:

a) If you blow up a _ _ _ _ _ _ _ _ _ _ _ _ too much, it might pop.

b) You might find plastic cows, sheep and chickens on a _ _ _ _ _ _   _ _ _ _ _ _ _ _ _.

c) With a set of _ _ _ _ _ _ _ _   _ _ _ _ _ _ _ you can talk to someone in another room.

d) The _ _ _ _ _ _ _ _ _   _ _ _ _ _ _ is the most common type of cuddly toy.

e) A _ _ _ _ _ _ _ _ _ _ _ _   _ _ _ _ _ _ is yellow and floats in the bath.

2. Discussion questions

a) What was your favourite toy when you were a child?

b) Do you think toys of the future will be similar to today's toys?

c) Do you think some toys aren't suitable for children?

39. Clothes

trousers

shirt

blouse

pyjamas

belt

coat

suit

slippers

t-shirt

dress

skirt

jumper / sweater

boots

high heels

hat

gloves

tights

scarf

cardigan

tracksuit

39.   Clothes

1. Complete the sentences:

a) A collar, sleeves, buttons and cuffs are all parts of a _ _ _ _ _ _ _ _.

b) A man might wear a _ _ _ _ _ _ _ to a wedding, a funeral or a job interview.

c) _ _ _ _ _ _ _ _ _ _ _ are clothes that are worn in bed.

d) A _ _ _ _ _ _ _ _ _ _ is another name for a woman's shirt.

e) You wear a _ _ _ _ _ _ _ round your trouser to stop them falling down.

2. Discussion questions

a) Where do you like to shop for clothes?

b) What's the most expensive item of clothing you've ever bought?

c) Are you embarrassed about any of your fashion choices from the past?

40. Accessories

belt

earrings

handbag

wallet

purse

sunglasses

scarf

gloves

tie

umbrella

watch

necklace

headphones

baseball cap

ring

bracelet

iPod

mobile phone

cuff links

lighter

40.   Accessories

1. Complete the sentences:

a) A _ _ _ _ _ _ _ _ _ _ _ _ _ _ is a piece of jewelry which is worn around the wrist.

b) A _ _ _ _ _ _ is worn around the collar of a shirt.

c) If it's raining, you'll need to carry an _ _ _ _ _ _ _ _ _ _ _ _ _ _.

d) Women usually keep their money in a _ _ _ _ _ _ _ while men carry a _ _ _ _ _ _ _ _.

e) _ _ _ _ _ _ _ _ keep your hands warm on a chilly day.

2. Discussion questions

a) What accessories do you have with you today?

b) What's your favourite accessory?

c) What accessories might people wear or carry in ten years' time?

41.   Music

punk rock

jazz

pop

rock

classical

CD

MP3

record player

song

verse

chorus

tune up

beat

techno

duet

hip hop

volume

guitar

bass

keyboard

41.   Music

1. Complete the sentences:

a) Turn up the _ _ _ _ _ _ _ _ _ _ _ if you want the music to be louder.

b) A _ _ _ _ _ _ _ _ _ _ _ _ _ _ is like an electric piano.

c) The _ _ _ _ _ _ _ _ _ _ _ is part of a song that is repeated between verses.

d) Beethoven, Bach and Mozart were _ _ _ _ _ _ _ _ _ _ _ _ _ _ music composers.

e) Some musicians need to _ _ _ _ _ _ _ _ _ _ _ _ their instruments before playing.

2. Discussion questions

a) What kind of music do you like?

b) What was the first or last concert you went to?

c) Do you think pop music was better when you were younger?

42.   The Movies

screen

cinema

science fiction

front row

popcorn

intermission

trailer

Oscar

box office

genre

comedy

drama

documentary

director

actor

plot

review

critic

scene

credits

42.

The Movies

1. Complete the sentences:

a) The _ _ _ _ _ _ _ _ _ _ _ _ _ _ is the boss on a film set.

b) The _ _ _ _ _ _ _ describes what happens in a film.

c) A _ _ _ _ _ _ _ _ _ is a professional opinion of a film or other art work.

d) A _ _ _ _ _ _ _ _ _ _ _ _ _ _ _ _ _ is a film about real life and real people.

e) A _ _ _ _ _ _ _ _ _ _ _ _ _ _ is a short preview of an upcoming film.

2. Discussion questions

a) What are some of your favourite films?

b) What was the last film you saw?

c) If you could have dinner with any actor or actress from any time, who would you choose?

43.   The Press

newspaper

editor

journalist

photographer

column

crossword

cartoon

magazine

report

headline

reviews

advertising

contents

interview

paparazzi

article

story

press release

obituary

quote

43.   The Press

1. Complete the sentences:

a) The _ _ _ _ _ _ _ _ _ _ decides what goes in a newspaper.

b) _ _ _ _ _ _ _ _ _ _ _ _ _ _ _ is a way for magazines and newspapers to make money.

c) A _ _ _ _ _ _ _ _ _ is the exact words spoken by someone.

d) An _ _ _ _ _ _ _ _ _ _ is when a journalist asks someone questions.

e) The _ _ _ _ _ _ _ _ _ _ _ _ _ _ is printed in big, bold letters above a news story.

2. Discussion questions

a) How do you keep up with the news?

b) What do you think of the press in your country?

c) What are the big stories in the news at the moment?

44.　Current Affairs

revolution

earthquake

strike

election

riot

demonstration

scandal

war

murder

robbery

fire

inflation

ceasefire

terrorist attack

assassination

unemployment

accident

stock market crash

discovery

the big match / game

44. Current Affairs

1. Complete the sentences:

a) _ _ _ _ _ _ _ _ _ _ _ _ _ _ _ _ _ is the murder of an important person, usually for

payment or political reasons

b) _ _ _ _ _ _ _ _ _ _ _ _ _ _ _ _ _ _ is a word describing people not having jobs.

c) A _ _ _ _ _ _ _ _ _ _ _ _ _ _ _ is when something new is found.

d) When a lot of people fight in the street, it is described as a _ _ _ _ _ _ _ _.

e) An _ _ _ _ _ _ _ _ _ _ _ is the process where a country decides democratically on a

new leader.

2. Discussion questions

a) Have you ever taken part in a demonstration?

b) Can you think of any recent scandals?

c) How healthy is your country's economy at the moment?

45.   Literature

paperback

author

review

page

paragraph

chapter

screenplay

fiction

non-fiction

poetry

eBook

comic book

novel

biography

diary

play

dictionary

index

classic

library

45.   Literature

1. Complete the sentences:

a) If you don't know the meaning of a word, look it up in a _ _ _ _ _ _ _ _ _ _ _ _ _ _ _ _ _.

b) A _ _ _ _ _ _ _ _ _ _ _ _ _ _ _ _ is a story with both pictures and text.

c) You can borrow books from a _ _ _ _ _ _ _ _ _ _ _ _ _ _.

d) You can often find specific information in a book by using the _ _ _ _ _ _ _ at the back.

e) _ _ _ _ _ _ _ _ _ _ _ _ _ _ _ _ describes a book which is about real people and events.

2. Discussion questions

a) What was the last good book you read?

b) Who are the most well-known writers from your country?

c) Have you ever read a book that made a great impression on you?

46.   Musical Instruments

guitar

bass guitar

drums

keyboard

flute

trumpet

xylophone

double bass

violin

harmonica

accordion

saxophone

tambourine

piano

organ

cello

trombone

castanets

cymbal

voice

46.   Musical Instruments

1. Complete the sentences:

a) Bang on the _ _ _ _ _ _ _ _ to create a nice beat.

b) A _ _ _ _ _ _ _ _ usually has 88 black and white keys.

c) A _ _ _ _ _ _ _ _ _ _ _ _ is a string instrument which is held against the neck and

   played with a bow.

d) You play an _ _ _ _ _ _ _ _ _ _ _ _ _ _ _ _ _ _ by squeezing it from both sides and

   pressing the right keys.

e) The _ _ _ _ _ _ _ _ _ _ _ _ _ _ _ _ _ _ looks like a very big guitar, it has four strings

   and you must usually play it standing up.

2. Discussion questions

a) Do you play any musical instruments?

b) If you could play any musical instrument, what would you choose?

c) Do you think it's important that children learn to play an instrument?

47.   Fruits and Vegetables

carrot

potato

cauliflower

lettuce

tomato

strawberry

apple

peas

pineapple

coconut

onion

garlic

banana

aubergine

courgette

grapefruit

mango

lemon

cherries

mushrooms

47. Fruits and Vegetables

1. Complete the sentences:

a) _ _ _ _ _ _ _ _ _ _ _ has green leaves and is often eaten raw in a salad.

b) _ _ _ _ _ _ _ _ _ _ _ _ _ _ _ grow in dark, damp places.

c) A _ _ _ _ _ _ _ _ _ _ _ _ _ looks like a big orange but is yellow and tastes a little sour.

d) _ _ _ _ _ _ _ _ _ are small, round, green and difficult to eat with a fork.

e) _ _ _ _ _ _ _ _ _ _ _ _ are small, round, red fruit which grows in trees.

2. Discussion questions

a) Are there any fruits or vegetables which you don't like.

b) Do you eat enough fruit and vegetables?

c) Have you ever considered becoming vegetarian?

48.   Drinks

cola

coffee

milk

cocktail

whisky

vodka

beer

sparkling wine

champagne

tea

water

hot chocolate

lemonade

juice

port

yoghurt

tequila

Jack Daniels

cappuccino

espresso

48.   Drinks

1. Complete the sentences:

a) _ _ _ _ _ is made by adding hot water to leaves from a certain plant.

b) _ _ _ _ _ _ _ _ _ _ _ is a drink made from sour milk.

c) _ is the most well-known sparkling wine.

d) A _ _ _ _ _ _ _ _ _ _ _ is a mixture of different drinks, usually alcoholic.

e) _ _ _ _ _ _ _ is a strong alcoholic drink which is associated with Scotland and Ireland.

2. Discussion questions

a) What are your favourite hot and cold drinks?

b) Do you know how to make any cocktails?

c) What drinks don't you like?

Snacks

chocolate bar

piece of fruit

biscuit

packet of crisps

burger

nuts

rice cake

energy bar

pizza

sandwich

popcorn

carrot stick

cheese

hot dog

doughnut

pie

quiche

yoghurt

banana

ice cream

49. Snacks

1. Complete the sentences:

a) _ _ _ _ _ _ _ _ _ _ _ is often eaten at the cinema.

b) A sausage in a bread roll is sometimes known as a _ _ _ _ _ _ _ _ _ _ _.

c) It's nice to eat an _ _ _ _ _ _ _ _ _ _ _ _ on a very hot day.

d) _ _ _ _ _ _ is made from pastry, cheese and other ingredients and comes from France.

e) A _ _ _ _ _ _ _ _ _ _ _ _ _ is a sugary snack, sometimes it has a hole in the middle.

2. Discussion questions

a) What are some of your favourite snacks?

b) Do you think you are a healthy eater?

c) What snacks are popular in your country?

50. At the Restaurant

knife

fork

spoon

salt and pepper

waiter

waitress

plate

cutlery

bill

receipt

dessert

main course

starter

digestif

specials board

napkin

tip

reservation

chef

doggie bag

50.   At the Restaurant

1. Complete the sentences:

a) You wipe your mouth with a _ _ _ _ _ _ _ _ _ _ after eating.

b) _ _ _ _ _ _ _ _ _ is something sweet to eat after the main course.

c) Knives, forks and spoons are items of _ _ _ _ _ _ _ _ _ _ _ _ _.

d) In many cultures it's customary to leave a _ _ _ _ _ _ to say thank you for the service.

e) Ask for the _ _ _ _ _ _ _ when you have finished your meal and are ready to leave.

2. Discussion questions

a) Do you have a favourite restaurant?

b) What do you think about tipping?

c) Have you ever been to a very expensive restaurant?

Answer Key

1 a) niece, b) father in law, c) grandchildren, d) aunt, e) cousins

2 a) social networks, b) podcast, c) URL, d) bookmark, e) the cloud

3 a) eBay, b) Wikipedia, c) Facebook, d) Bing, PayPal

4 a) cable, b) font, c) driver, d) spam, e) crash

5 a) decorator, b) entrepreneur, c) illustrator, d)travel agent, e) vet

6 a) shredder, b) filing cabinet, c) open plan, d) fax machine, e) office draw

7 a) scissors, b) stamp, c) stapler / paperclip, d) ruler, e) post it note

8 a) gravity, b) safety goggles, c) equation, d) acid, e) ventilator

9 a) Gillette, b) Ikea, c) Disney, d) Coca Cola & Pepsi, e) Levi's

10 a) confidential, b) deal, c) attendees, d) the minutes, e) chart

11 a) court, b) judge, c) witness, d) evidence, e) prison

12 a) fine, b) counterfeiter, c) burglar, d) death penalty, e) identity theft

13 a) wages, b) currency, c) interest, d) gift voucher, e) deposit

14 a) giraffe, b) penguin, c) owl, d) cheetah, e) zebra

15 a) sheep & clouds, b) rainbow, c) sunset, d) view, e) wildlife

16 a) submarine, b) lighthouse, c) tanker, d) shark, e) harbour

17 a) parachute, b) missile, c) frisbee, d) planets, e) helicopter

18 a) motorbike, b) jet ski, c) ferry, d) tank, e) sledge

19 a) rear view mirror, b) reverse, c) accelerator, d) speedometer, e) indicator

20 a) accommodation, b) passport, c) customs, d) reservation, e) hike

21 a) India, b) Scotland, c)Canada, d) Germany, e) Brazil

22 a) conditioner, b) razor, c) deodorant, d) towel, e) plug

23 a) microwave, b) teaspoon, c) kettle, d) blender, e) oven glove

24 a) clothes, b) make-up, c) slippers, d) curtains, e) pillow

25 a) kite, b) axe, c) wheelbarrow, d) freezer, e) ladder

26 a) greenhouse, b) spade, c) weeds, d) path, e) squirrel

27 a) sprint, b) tennis, c) Monopoly, d) pool, e) chess

28 a) treadmill, b) trampolining, c) weight lifting, d) gym, e) boxing

29 a) DIY, b) drawing, c) pottery, d) calligraphy, e) gardening

30 a) cocktail, b) art gallery, c) casino, d) bowling, e) karaoke

31 a) queue, b) receipt, c) dairy product, d) special offer, e) out of stock

32 a) Jeweler, b) DIY store, c) florist, d) tailor, e) butcher

33 a) post box, b) bridge, c) pedestrians, d) traffic warden, e) road sign

34 a) stocking, b) carol, c) Boxing Day, d) candle, e) sleigh

35 a) Yuri Gagarin, b) Pele, c) Paul McCartney, d) Bob Marley, e) Marilyn Monroe

36 a) housewarming, b) stag night, c) engagement, d) Ramadan, e) retirement

37 a) safety goggles, b) sandpaper, c) glue, d) drill, e) hammer

38 a) balloon, b) toy farm, c) walkie talkies, d) teddy bear, e) rubber duck

39 a) shirt, b) suit, c) pyjamas, d) blouse, e) belt

40 a) bracelet, b) tie, c) umbrella, d) purse, belt, e) gloves

41 a) volume, b) keyboard, c) chorus, d) classical, e) tune up

42 a) director, b) plot, c) review, d) documentary, e) trailer

43 a) editor, b) advertising, c) quote, d) interview, e) headline

44 a) assassination, b) unemployment, c) discovery, d) riot, e) election

45 a) dictionary, b) comic book, c) library, d) index, e) non-fiction

46 a) drum, b) piano, c) violin, d) accordion, e) double bass

47 a) lettuce, b) mushrooms, c) grapefruit, d) peas, e) cherries

48 a) tea, b) yoghurt, c) champagne, d) cocktail, e) whisky

49 a) popcorn, b) hot dog, c) ice cream, d) quiche, e) doughnut

50 a) napkin, b) dessert, c) cutlery, d) tip, e) bill